Theory Paper   Grade 6   2014   A

Duration 3 hours

Candidates should answer all FIVE questions.
Write your answers on this paper – no others will be accepted.
Answers must be written clearly and neatly – otherwise marks may be lost.

1   Answer **ONE** section only, (a) or (b).

15

EITHER

(a)   Indicate **ONE** chord at each of the places marked ∗ to accompany the following melody. You may do so by writing roman numerals or any other recognized method of notation between the staves, **OR** by writing notes on the staves which provide a proper harmonic structure; but use only **ONE** of these methods.

J. Clarke, Hymn Tune, *Uffingham* (adapted)

3

OR

(b) Complete the bass line and add a suitable figured bass as necessary, *from the first beat of bar 3*, at the places marked * in this passage. If you wish to use a $\frac{5}{3}$ chord, leave the space under the asterisk blank, but $\frac{5}{3}$ chords *must* be shown when used as part of a $\frac{6}{4}\frac{5}{3}$ progression or when chromatic alteration is required.

2 Writing for four-part voices (SATB) or keyboard, realize this figured bass. Assume that all chords are $\frac{5}{3}$ unless otherwise shown.

15

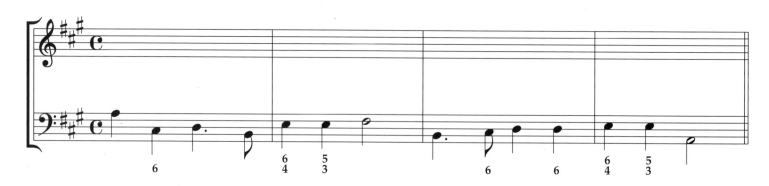

Music Theory Past Papers 2014

ABRSM Grade 6

3 EITHER

(a) Continue this opening to form a complete melody for unaccompanied violin. It should end with a modulation to the dominant and should be between eight and ten bars long. Add performance directions as appropriate and write the complete melody on the staves below.

Menuet   Haydn

OR

(b) Continue this opening for unaccompanied bassoon to make a complete piece of not less than eight bars in length. You may make any modulation(s) that you wish, or none if you prefer. Add performance directions as appropriate and write the complete melody on the staves below.

Andante

Hark! Hark, what I tell to Thee: no sor-row o'er the tomb, no __ sor-row o-ver the tomb!

My spi - rit wanders free, my spi - rit wanders free and waits, and __ waits, till __ etc.

4 Look at the extract printed opposite, which is from a song, and then answer the questions below. 25

(a) Mark **clearly** on the score, using the appropriate capital letter for identification, one example of each of the following. Also give the bar number(s) of each of your answers. The first answer is given.

From bar 20 onwards

A   a bar where the alto sings a note at a lower pitch than the top note of the right-hand piano part (circle the note concerned).   Bar ...23....

B   a rising chromatic semitone (augmented unison) in the right-hand piano part (circle the notes concerned).   Bar(s) .... (2)

C   a melodic interval of a diminished 7th in the left-hand piano part (circle the notes concerned).   Bar .... (2)

(b) Write out in full the right-hand piano part of bar 20 as you think it should be played.

(3)

(c) Identify the chords marked * *in the piano part* of bars 15 and 17 by writing on the dotted lines below. Use either words or symbols. For each chord, indicate the position and show whether it is major, minor, augmented or diminished.

Bar 15   ....

Bar 17   ....

} Key: F minor   (6)

(d) Give the full names of the notes of melodic decoration (e.g. upper auxiliary note) marked **X**, **Y** and **Z**.

X (right-hand piano part, bar 8)   .... (2)

Y (alto, bar 23)   .... (2)

Z (alto, bar 31)   .... (2)

(e) Name two similarities and two differences between bars 1–4 and bars 11–14.

Similarities   1   .... (1)

2   .... (1)

Differences   1   .... (1)

2   .... (1)

(f) From the list below, underline the name of the most likely composer of this extract and give a reason for your answer.

J. S. Bach   Haydn   Chopin   Debussy   (1)

Reason: .... (1)

5 Look at the extract printed on pages 9–10, which is from Dvořák's *Symphonic Variations*, and then answer the questions below.

25

   (a) Give the meaning of:

      Larghetto .... (2)

      ritard. (bar 6) .... (2)

      arco (bar 7, cellos) .... (2)

   (b) (i) Write out the parts for horns in bars 3–4 as they would sound at concert pitch and using the given clefs.

        (3)

     (ii) In this extract, the parts for clarinets are in C. Using the blank stave at the foot of page 10, write out the part for first clarinet in bars 7–8 *as it would appear at written pitch* for a clarinet *in B♭*. Do *not* use a key signature. (2)

   (c) Complete the following statements:

     (i) The largest melodic interval in the flute part is a(n) .... (2)

     (ii) The rhythm played by the flute in bar 1 is later repeated by the .... and the .... (2)

     (iii) The instruments *sounding* in unison with the violas on the third quaver of bar 7 are

        the .... and the .... (2)

   (d) Describe fully the numbered and bracketed harmonic intervals *sounding* between:

     1 cellos and second clarinet, bar 4 .... (2)

     2 violas and first horn, bar 7 .... (2)

   (e) Answer TRUE or FALSE to each of the following statements:

     (i) The bassoons and violas sound in unison on the first beat of bars 1 and 2. .... (2)

     (ii) The flute plays a lower mordent in bar 4. .... (2)

(b) (ii)
bars 7–8   Clarinet 1

Theory Paper   Grade 6   2014   B

TOTAL MARKS
100

Duration 3 hours

Candidates should answer all FIVE questions.
Write your answers on this paper – no others will be accepted.
Answers must be written clearly and neatly – otherwise marks may be lost.

1   Answer **ONE** section only, (a) or (b).

15

EITHER

(a) Indicate **ONE** chord at each of the places marked * to accompany the following melody. You may do so by writing roman numerals or any other recognized method of notation between the staves, **OR** by writing notes on the staves which provide a proper harmonic structure; but use only **ONE** of these methods.

[Moderato]   Traditional English Melody

OR

(b) Complete the bass line and add a suitable figured bass as necessary, *from the first beat of bar 3*, at the places marked * in this passage. If you wish to use a ⁵₃ chord, leave the space under the asterisk blank, but ⁵₃ chords *must* be shown when used as part of a ⁶₄ ⁵₃ progression or when chromatic alteration is required.

Allegro

Handel, Sonata in B flat, HWV 357

2 Writing for four-part voices (SATB) or keyboard, realize this figured bass. Assume that all chords are ⁵₃ unless otherwise shown.

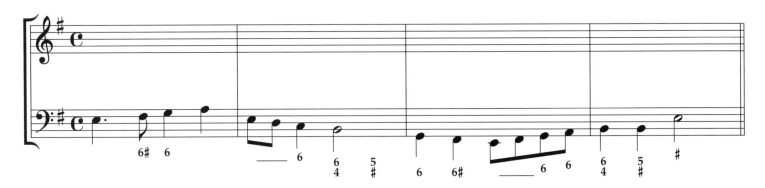

3 EITHER

(a) Continue this opening to form a complete melody for unaccompanied oboe. It should end with a modulation to the relative major and should be between eight and ten bars long. Add performance directions as appropriate and write the complete melody on the staves below.

Andante scherzando   Mendelssohn

OR

(b) Continue this opening for unaccompanied trombone to make a complete piece of not less than eight bars in length. You may make any modulation(s) that you wish, or none if you prefer. Add performance directions as appropriate and write the complete melody on the staves below.

Andante deciso

4 Look at the extract printed opposite, which is from a piece for piano, and then answer the questions below.

(a) Give the meaning of:

ben legato (bar 1)   ....   (2)

sotto voce (bar 13)   ....   (2)

(b) Identify the chords marked * in bars 2 and 14 by writing on the dotted lines below. Use either words or symbols. For each chord, indicate the position, show whether it is major, minor, augmented or diminished, and name the prevailing key.

Bar 2   ....   Key   ....   (4)

Bar 14   ....   Key   ....   (4)

(c) Mark **clearly** on the score, using the appropriate capital letter for identification, one example of each of the following. Also give the bar number(s) of each of your answers. The first answer is given.

In bars 1–12

A   a descending chromatic semitone (augmented unison) in the left-hand part (circle the notes concerned).   Bar ....⁴....

B   a melodic interval of a major 6th in the top line of the right-hand part (circle the notes concerned).   Bars ....   (2)

C   an augmented triad in first inversion (circle the notes concerned).   Bar ....   (2)

D   a harmonic interval of a diminished 5th in the right-hand part (circle the notes concerned).   Bar ....   (2)

(d) Name four features of the music that contribute to the change of mood at bar 13.

1   ....   (1)

2   ....   (1)

3   ....   (1)

4   ....   (1)

(e) From the list below, underline one period during which you think this piece was written and give two reasons for your answer.

                  1650–1750   1750–1850   1850–1950   (1)

Reasons

1   ....   (1)

2   ....   (1)

5 Look at the extract printed opposite, which is from the third movement of Lennox Berkeley's *Partita* for chamber orchestra, and then answer the questions below.

   (a) Give the meaning of:

      V (e.g. bar 5, second violins) .... (2)

      port. (portamento) (e.g. bars 5–6, first violins) .... (2)

      pizz. (bar 6, cellos) .... (2)

   (b) (i) Write out the parts for horns in bar 3 as they would sound at concert pitch and using the given clefs.

                                                                                                 (4)

      (ii) Write out the parts for clarinets in bar 5 as they would sound at concert pitch and using the given clefs.

                                                                                                  (3)

   (c) Complete the following statements:

      (i) The letter name of the
lowest-sounding note in bar 4 is .... and it is played by the .... (2)

      (ii) The letter name of the
highest-sounding note in bar 6 is .... and it is played by the .... (2)

   (d) Describe fully the numbered and bracketed harmonic intervals *sounding* between:

      1 trombone and bassoon, bar 5 .... (2)

      2 violas and second clarinet, bar 6 .... (2)

   (e) Answer TRUE or FALSE to each of the following statements:

      (i) The string instruments do not have to play an open string in this extract. .... (2)

      (ii) In bars 6–7 the trumpet plays an exact
repetition a semitone lower of its part in bars 1–2. .... (2)

BLANK PAGE

Theory Paper   Grade 6   2014   C

Duration 3 hours

Candidates should answer all FIVE questions.
Write your answers on this paper – no others will be accepted.
Answers must be written clearly and neatly – otherwise marks may be lost.

TOTAL MARKS
100

1 Answer ONE section only, (a) or (b).

15

EITHER

(a) Indicate ONE chord at each of the places marked * to accompany the following melody. You may do so by writing roman numerals or any other recognized method of notation between the staves, OR by writing notes on the staves which provide a proper harmonic structure; but use only ONE of these methods.

Stanley, Voluntary Op. 5 No. 3 (adapted)

OR

(b) Complete the bass line and add a suitable figured bass as necessary, *from the third beat of bar 2*, at the places marked * in this passage. If you wish to use a $\frac{5}{3}$ chord, leave the space under the asterisk blank, but $\frac{5}{3}$ chords *must* be shown when used as part of a $\frac{6}{4}\ \frac{5}{3}$ progression or when chromatic alteration is required.

Moderato   Handel, Aria from *Alexander's Feast* (adapted)

2 Writing for four-part voices (SATB) or keyboard, realize this figured bass. Assume that all chords are $\frac{5}{3}$ unless otherwise shown.

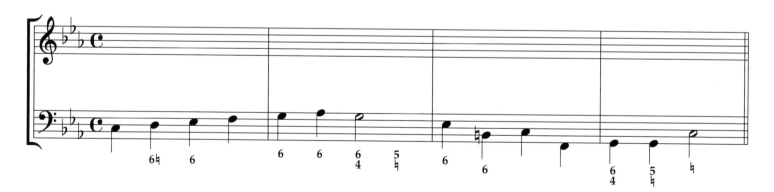

3 EITHER

(a) Continue this opening to form a complete melody for unaccompanied cello. It should end with a modulation to the subdominant and should be between eight and ten bars long. Add performance directions as appropriate and write the complete melody on the staves below.

Allegro energico e con fuoco

Mendelssohn

OR

(b) Continue this opening for unaccompanied clarinet to make a complete piece of not less than eight bars in length. You may make any modulation(s) that you wish, or none if you prefer. Add performance directions as appropriate and write the complete melody on the staves below.

Andante con moto

4 Look at the extract printed opposite, which is from a piece for keyboard, and then answer the questions below. 25

(a) Give the meaning of 𝄵 (e.g. bar 2, right-hand part). .... (2)

(b) The opening phrase of the right-hand part (marked ⌐‾‾‾‾‾‾‾‾‾⌐) is repeated in bars 3–4 (marked ∟_____⌐), three differences being:

 1 .... (1)

 2 .... (1)

 3 .... (1)

(c) Identify the chords marked ∗ in bars 6 and 11 by writing on the dotted lines below. Use either words or symbols. For each chord, indicate the position, show whether it is major, minor, augmented or diminished, and name the prevailing key.

 Bar 6 .... Key .... (4)

 Bar 11 .... Key .... (4)

(d) Mark **clearly** on the score, using the appropriate capital letter for identification, one example of each of the following. Also give the bar number(s) of each of your answers. The first answer is given.

 From bar 6 onwards

 A a melodic interval of a minor 7th in the right-hand part (circle the notes concerned). Bar ....8....

 B three successive bars in the right-hand part that form a descending melodic sequence (not exact) (mark ⌐ **B** ⌐ over the bars). Bars .... (2)

 C a harmonic interval of a major 3rd in the left-hand part (circle the notes concerned). Bar .... (2)

 D an upper auxiliary note in the left-hand part (circle the note concerned). Bar .... (2)

 E a note of anticipation in the right-hand part (circle the note concerned). Bar .... (2)

(e) Write out in full the right-hand part of bar 10 as you think it should be played.

(3)

(f) From the list below, underline one period during which you think this piece was written.

 1700–1800   1800–1900   1900–2000 (1)

5 Look at the extract printed on pages 25–26, which is from the overture to *Die Fledermaus* by Johann Strauss, and then answer the questions below.

(a) Give the meaning of:

Tamburo .... (2)

Cassa .... (2)

(b) (i) Write out the parts for clarinets in bars 5–6 as they would sound at concert pitch.

(3)

(ii) Using the blank stave at the foot of page 26, write out the parts for horns in bars 8–9 as they would sound at concert pitch. (3)

(c) Name three features of the music that contribute to the change of mood from bar 12 onwards.

1 .... (1)

2 .... (1)

3 .... (1)

(d) Mark **clearly** on the score, using the appropriate capital letter for identification, one example of each of the following. Also give the bar number of each of your answers. The first answer is given.

In bars 1–7

A a rising chromatic semitone (augmented unison) in a part for a string instrument (circle the notes concerned). Bar ....1....

B a place where the violas sound at a lower pitch than the cellos (circle the notes concerned). Bar .... (2)

C a double stop that forms an interval of a diminished 5th in a string part (circle the notes concerned). Bar .... (2)

D a melodic interval of a perfect 4th in a non-transposing woodwind part (circle the notes concerned). Bar .... (2)

(e) Complete the following statement:

The instruments *sounding* in unison with the cellos on the first note of bar 14 are the

.... and the .... (2)

(f) Answer TRUE or FALSE to the following statements:

(i) The oboe and first violins sound in unison in bars 7–9. .... (2)

(ii) The chord formed by the notes *sounding* on the final quaver of bar 7 is a dominant 7th in root position (V^7a) in the key of E minor. .... (2)

(b) (ii)
bars 8–9

Horns 1 2

Theory Paper   Grade 6   2014   S

TOTAL MARKS
100

Duration 3 hours

Candidates should answer all FIVE questions.
Write your answers on this paper – no others will be accepted.
Answers must be written clearly and neatly – otherwise marks may be lost.

1   Answer ONE section only, (a) or (b).

15

EITHER

(a) Indicate ONE chord at each of the places marked * to accompany the following melody. You may do so by writing roman numerals or any other recognized method of notation between the staves, OR by writing notes on the staves which provide a proper harmonic structure; but use only ONE of these methods.

[Andante]   Traditional French carol

OR

(b) Complete the bass line and add a suitable figured bass as necessary, *from the third beat of bar 1*, at the places marked ∗ in this passage. If you wish to use a $\frac{5}{3}$ chord, leave the space under the asterisk blank, but $\frac{5}{3}$ chords *must* be shown when used as part of a $\frac{6}{4}\frac{5}{3}$ progression or when chromatic alteration is required.

[Moderato]

Handel, Aria from *Alexander's Feast* (adapted)

2 Writing for four-part voices (SATB) or keyboard, realize this figured bass.
Assume that all chords are $\frac{5}{3}$ unless otherwise shown.

15

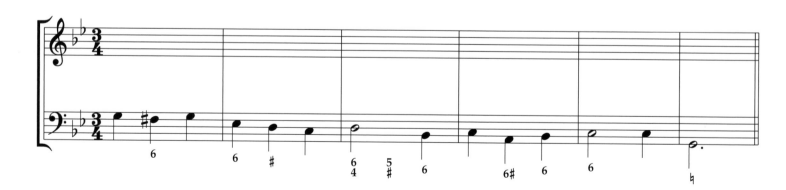

3 EITHER

(a) Continue this opening to form a complete melody for unaccompanied bassoon. It should end with a modulation to the relative minor and should be between eight and ten bars long. Add performance directions as appropriate and write the complete melody on the staves below.

Allegro moderato   Borodin (adapted)

p espressivo

OR

(b) Continue this opening for unaccompanied violin to make a complete piece of not less than eight bars in length. You may make any modulation(s) that you wish, or none if you prefer. Add performance directions as appropriate and write the complete melody on the staves below.

Alla gavotta

f

4 Look at the extract printed opposite, which is from J. Field's Nocturne in D minor, and then answer the questions below.

(a) Give the meaning of *dolente*. .... (2)

(b) Write out in full the top right-hand part of bar 19 as you think it should be played.

(3)

(c) Identify the chords marked * in bars 3 (shaded) and 9 by writing on the dotted lines below. Use either words or symbols. For each chord, indicate the position, show whether it is major, minor, augmented or diminished, and name the prevailing key.

Bar 3 .... Key .... (4)

Bar 9 .... Key .... (4)

(d) Mark **clearly** on the score, using the appropriate capital letter for identification, one example of each of the following. Also give the bar number(s) of each of your answers. The first answer is given.

In bars 8–16

A a melodic interval of a diminished 4th in
the left-hand part (circle the notes concerned). Bar ...15....

B melodic imitation between the hands across two bars. Bars .... (2)

C three consecutive harmonic intervals of a minor 3rd
in the left-hand part (circle the notes concerned). Bar .... (2)

D an imperfect cadence (IVb–V) in the tonic key. Bars .... (2)

E a melodic interval of a perfect 5th in the top line
of the right-hand part (circle the notes concerned). Bar .... (2)

(e) Give the full names of the notes of melodic decoration (e.g. note of anticipation) marked **X** and **Y**:

X (right hand, bar 14) .... (2)

Y (left hand, bar 16) .... (2)

5 Look at the extract printed on pages 33–34, which is from Kodály's *Nyári este*, and then answer the questions below.

(a) Give the meaning of:

div. (e.g. bar 4, second violins) .... (2)

pizz. (e.g. bar 13, cellos) .... (2)

(b) (i)   Write out the part for horn in bars 4–5 as it would sound at concert pitch.

Horn

(3)

(ii)   Using the blank stave on page 34, write out the parts for clarinets in bars 11–13 as they would sound at concert pitch. (4)

(c) Complete the following statements:

(i)   The instrument sounding in unison with the violas on the first quaver of bar 11 is the .... (2)

(ii)   From bar 10 onwards the second violins and violas sound notes in unison in bar(s) .... (2)

(iii) The harmonic interval *sounding* between the horn and cor anglais on the first beat of bar 7 is a(n) .... (2)

(d) Mark **clearly** on the score, using the appropriate capital letter for identification, one example of each of the following. Also give the bar number(s) of each of your answers. The first answer is given.

In bars 1–5

A   a note in the horn part which is marked to be held for its full value (circle the note concerned).   Bar ....3....

B   two consecutive notes in the second violin part that show a note and its enharmonic equivalent (circle the notes concerned).   Bar(s) .... (2)

C   a double stop that forms the interval of a major 6th (circle the notes concerned).   Bar .... (2)

(e) Answer TRUE or FALSE to each of the following statements:

(i)   There is syncopation in the viola part in every bar of this extract. .... (2)

(ii)   The violas play a pedal note (not sustained) on B♮ lasting for over six bars. .... (2)

(b) (ii)
bars 11–13